MANAGING DEATH AND BEREAVEMENT
A framework for caring organisations

Samia al Qadhi

the POLICY

P ~ P

PRESS

First published in Great Britain in 1996 by

The Policy Press
University of Bristol
Rodney Lodge
Grange Road
Bristol BS8 4EA

Telephone: (0117) 973 8797
Fax: (0117) 973 7308
E-mail: tpp@bris.ac.uk

ISBN 1 86134 014 1

Samia al Qadhi is the Director of a national cancer charity.

The *Policy Innovations* series has been established to present fresh ideas in the field of policy studies in a concise and cost-effective way, and provides a means of disseminating valuable ideas quickly and sometimes, though not exclusively, from new researchers.

The Policy Press works to counter discrimination on grounds of gender, race, disability, age and sexuality.

Printed in Great Britain by Bourne Press Ltd.

Summary

The object of this paper is to explore the issue of managing staff in organisations which work with the dying and to make recommendations for strategies for managing multiple bereavements. I make two basic assumptions about our working lives. First, that work must be seen as part of our overall experience of life and not as a separate contained entity. Second, that emotions are part of work and must be a consideration of management. I explore the context in which we work when managing multiple bereavements, by outlining the prevailing attitudes to death in British society, theories on grief and bereavement, the organisations which tend to work with the dying and how change and loss generally affect organisations. Within this context I explore ways of managing staff who are experiencing multiple bereavements and how to develop management strategies accordingly. My findings form recommendations for best practice and are briefly as follows:

- to understand the social context for death and dying;
- to understand grief and loss processes and the emotional reactions that arise in oneself and others;
- to develop an appropriate recruitment and training process;
- to create an atmosphere that allows the expression of emotion;
- to challenge denial and to acknowledge feelings;
- to use ritual where it is helpful;
- to consider boundary issues;
- to encourage mutual support;
- to develop practical support systems within organisations;
- to develop policies which reinforce these strategies;
- to develop practical support systems and policies which reinforce these strategies.

Acknowledgement

There are many people I would like to thank who contributed to this work. I am particularly indebted to those people who agreed to talk to me about their own experience of managing death. I would also like to thank those I have known who have died. They are the ones who allowed me to learn with them, in some ways at their expense. In this group most of all I thank Dave. I hope this exploration contains the sensitivity and integrity their sharing with me deserves.

Contents

Foreword   7

Introduction   9
     Objectives   9
     Why manage death?   10

Methodology   15
     Personal experience   15
     Interviews   16
     Publications and research   17

My own experience   18
     Motivations   18
     My mechanisms for coping   19

The context   21
     The prevailing attitudes to death   21
     Theories on grief and bereavement   24
     Cultures within caring organisations   27
     Change and loss in organisations   30

Contributing factors   32
     Staff motivation   33
     Emotions engendered   35
     Self-identification and professionalism   37

Management strategies   39
     Context and theory   39
     Self-awareness   39
     Recruitment and training   40
     Freedom to express emotion   41
     Challenge denial and acknowledge grief   43
     The role of ritual   46
     Boundaries   47
     Mutual support   49
     Practical support and policies   50

Conclusion   54

Postscript   *56*

References and further reading   *57*

Foreword

The following extract is from my diary written in 1990.

It feels so important to keep going day after day with nothing new to say, no mutual experience to build upon except our common knowledge of the situation. To bring food, flowers, entertainment, news from the outside world, to share the time together. Hoping to bring love and with it strength and thus a will to live, all in the apparently hopeless belief that this time if I try hard enough I might help this person beat this virus. If I can help the person want to live enough, they might. Then gradually I know that again I am being beaten, I can't stop or control this meaningless invisible enemy and that by pressurising the person I love to keep resisting, I am making their struggle harder. There comes a time, it seems, when death can become the only tolerable option. There comes a time when relaxing into the situation seems to be the only way. Watching this, sharing it where I can, is probably the hardest thing I have ever done. When the person I love no longer wishes to fight, I stop visiting to be with them and be an ally in their fight. I visit to be with them while they die, to hold them, to breathe with them, to sleep, to maybe give them some of my peace, to try to share in some of the fear and pain, to accept their death at their pace, to let them go when they are ready and, if they wish me to, to go some of the way with them. Maybe if I can face it a bit with them, it won't be quite so frightening or lonely.

I know it is a very subjective viewpoint. Maybe what is right for me is not right for others. I can't help but try to give to the people I love who are dying what I think I would want to receive. I know that I have the courage to give support and I also have the courage to ask people what they want and to hear them when they answer.

So much has changed. I no longer feel immortal. I sometimes feel terrified of my own death, convinced I have HIV or cancer and will die soon. I also have great fear of my family's death. I don't really remember who I was before all this, what I understood of myself and the world. I am reminded of a sentence in Susan Sontag's book, *The way we live now*, where she writes, "whatever happened it was over, the way we had lived until now, the end of bravado, the end of folly, the end of trusting life, the end of taking life for granted, and of treating life as something that, Samurai-like, he thought himself ready to throw away lightly, impudently".

I feel now I see some clarity, some purpose, to learn, to love and to feel. I feel very lucky. At the risk of using a cliché and sounding repulsively self-satisfied, I feel I have no business to come into people's lives during such a significant time, to be involved in their death. Sometimes I feel a fraud, a voyeur, as if I'm taking out more than I give in. I haven't resolved these feelings, I don't know if I'm doing the right thing, but I will keep struggling to find out. Sometimes I think I will leave this sort of work when I understand the answer to some of my questions. I think writing about them might be an end to this process.

Introduction

Objectives

This paper sets out to explore the issues which arise in environments of multiple bereavements and to make recommendations for management strategies for best practice in these organisations. My inquiry concerns what managers can do for themselves and for the organisations they have a stake in. It aims to address issues that arise as a result of the deaths within the organisation. These deaths include both those of users of services and staff. I make two basic assumptions in this inquiry. First, that work must be seen in the context of our overall lives and not as a separate entity. Second, that emotions are part of work and must be a consideration of management. I investigate the varieties of ways organisations which experience multiple bereavements address the issue of death and explore what developments might be most useful and effective. Central to this inquiry is the question of whether a theory of best practice is transferable or whether the practice is tied to the culture of the specific organisation. I conclude with some recommendations for the management of bereavement within organisations. An organisation dealing with multiple loss can and should have policies, procedures and guidelines which address issues relating to death. Management have a responsibility to staff and themselves to minimise the negative emotions resulting from multiple bereavements, particularly those which might have long-term effects.

A number of issues arise in this arena, such as: living while dying; working with people who are dying, ill or potentially ill; how this affects ourselves and others; realisation of mortality; and the impact of multiple deaths. This paper puts these issues in the different contexts of effects on individuals, groups, sub-cultures and organisations or institutions. In asking what is best practice in organisations which experience multiple deaths I am asking what managers can and should do to ensure death is handled as well as possible in a work environment.

This paper does not explore how organisations in general deal with death. Although this would be interesting, to cover it in full would widen my inquiry too much. Thus, incidental deaths within organisations and the management thereof are not included. However, some of my recommendations apply generally to the management of death and loss within all sorts of organisations. The other areas I have chosen not to explore fully are the wider issues of grief and bereavement.

There is an enormous amount written on those topics, and though I use some of this work and refer to it I have not attempted to add to this thinking. The area I have identified and do wish to comment upon is multiple deaths and bereavement within organisations and potential responses to them.

Having outlined the central objective of this inquiry it is important to explore a further objective. As a participant in the organisations with which I am concerned, I am deeply involved with and emotionally affected by the experience of multiple bereavements. I decided to write this paper because I am fascinated by the issues and have been profoundly affected by the grief I have consequently experienced. I make no apology for this lack of objectivity and call upon my own experience throughout the work, attempting to explain my perspective. However, I also call upon the experience of others in order to bring some balance to the inquiry. The combination of my own experience and the resources of others should produce some useful conclusions. This model of inquiry is discussed by Reason and Marshall (Boud and Griffin, 1987, p 113). They examine the role of research in contributing to knowledge and identify three objectives: the role of research for the reader, 'for them'; the role of research as 'cooperative endeavour', 'for us'; and the role of research as a 'contribution to personal development', 'for me'. This model suits my purposes in that the research contributes to the knowledge in an academic sense, part of the cooperative process of exploring this issue within organisations and also part of my own personal process of dealing with this experience. I return to this issue in the section on methodology.

Why manage death?

Why should managers concern themselves with the issue of bereavement? In many ways organisations have traditionally seen emotional issues for staff as beyond their domain. My experience and research has brought me to believe that there are some useful techniques when dealing with multiple deaths within an organisation. As a result of considering these issues and implementing some systems accordingly, members of organisations would be able to come to terms with multiple deaths, to continue to work in this context and not to take unnecessary absence from work, and when they do leave, not to be burdened with the long-term negative emotional affects of their work. As one of my four interviewees (the Nurse Educator) said

It means being able to keep doing the work over a long period of time and it means changing as time goes on. It means less use of defence mechanisms and an increased ability to be open to inquiry and to be non-defensive. And it means being able to enjoy the work.

The process was well summed up by the Charge Nurse as "helping the staff to feel looked after and be looked after in order for them to be able to get on with looking after the patients".

Research has shown that people leave organisations that care for the dying because "the constant exposure to death and the accumulation of multiple deaths left them feeling either depressed or burned out" (Vachon). Many might argue that investing in managing the effects of multiple bereavement is too expensive. However, in a San Francisco AIDS project "A cost-benefit analysis of a Staff Care Plan ... found that the plan is likely to meet its objectives of reducing burnout and being cost effective, despite a projected cost of as much as $157,000" (Schoen, 1992, p 7). I also believe that members of organisations and managers within them have a mutual moral and social responsibility to address this form of loss, a view which was reinforced by the Charge Nurse who believed "it's moral and it's ethical, you should look after people".

I have made a basic assumption that is consistent with this perspective. I see work as a fully integral part of employed people's lives. Attempts are sometimes made to divorce the experience of work from the wider experience of life and often people who work choose to disassociate themselves from their experience of themselves at work for a number of reasons. This might include people experiencing work as unfulfilling or not validating. My experience has led me to believe that this distinction is not possible and I would further argue that the attempt to separate emotions from our experience of work is counter-productive. People are themselves wherever they are, even if they are presenting differently in different environments. As Charles-Edwards writes "The whole person is there in both life segments" (1992, p 4). I see the energy expended on presenting different fronts as a cause of stress in itself. Organisational cultures often attempt to prevent connections being made between the emotional individual and the organisation. Many structural, rational, procedural and legal methods are used within bureaucracies in order to prevent what is perceived as the potential chaos of individualism, almost as if managers fear anarchy within organisations. Clegg refers to this as "the iron cage of bureaucracy" (Clegg, 1990, p 29). He discusses Weber's theory about organisation: "In Weber's view bureaucracy is to be regarded almost as if it were a scientific creation which has devoured its human creators", that "its humanity was fatefully compromised by its technical functioning" (Clegg, 1990, p 30).

Organisations are made up of a number of individuals and all the complex emotions that come with them. Emotions which arise within work will impact upon people's wider lives, thus emotions and organisations are inextricably linked. As James writes in her paper, "emotion needs to be established as a fitting subject for inclusion in academic discussion, and ... the idea that emotion can involve labour needs to be explored" (James, 1989, p 16). James' argument is that the separation of emotion and feeling from work is false and that the emotional work occurs in spite of the attempt to rationalise it out of the workplace. This ideology which makes the connections between emotions and organisations is increasingly acceptable today. Fineman's collection of papers (Fineman, 1993) is an example of the growing discussion on the issue. He argues that "emotions are within the texture of organising" (Fineman, 1993, p 1). An American perspective on this can be found in work by Puckett and Emery who argue "employers have the credibility to effectively communicate and objectively handle emotional and controversial subjects, and they have the financial motivation to take advantage of opportunities for disease prevention" (Puckett and Emery, 1988, p 87).

My view that work and feelings are inextricably linked is consistent with the various objectives of this inquiry. There is a personal process for myself throughout this paper. Similarly, I believe that there is little distinction between the private and public arenas of home and work – feelings will exist in both areas.

Given this hypothesis it is imperative that we manage multiple bereavements within organisations. The emotions of those who work in organisations which involve caring for the ill and dying will be profoundly affected by this experience. The emotional impact, such as realisation of mortality, fear of illness and pain, fear of death, burnout and stress, will affect their home life and their ability to carry out their work. There will also be a cumulative impact from the multiple deaths experienced. If managers wish people to work effectively and efficiently, then their experience of these deaths must be addressed. As Vachon puts it, "if patient care staff only give of themselves without in some way being replenished, they will ultimately have nothing left to give" (Corr and Corr, 1983, p 238). An organisation which does not support its workers in their experience of multiple deaths will be affected both financially and in the quality of care and service it provides. This will manifest itself in a number of ways, such as, a high level of absence, depression or staff burnout. Burnout as a concept in this context is well defined by Maslach as "a syndrome of emotional exhaustion, depersonalisation and reduced personal accomplishment that can occur among individuals that do 'people work' of some kind" (Maslach, 1982, p 3). The emotional aspect of the work is evident and I have both experienced and witnessed depersonalisation.

Burnout and accumulated grief can be avoided and emotions are manageable in ways that I shall explain in this paper. The practical, ethical and financial reasons for doing so are the motivation to create an efficient sustainable organisation with a high quality of service and good staff morale. It is also the case that staff who are well supported when bereaved will be more likely to be able to provide mutual support to colleagues (Charles-Edwards, 1992), thus compounding the positive effect. As Schoen argues in her work on AIDS organisations in the US, "grief, traditionally thought of as a personal matter, must become a concern of organisations" (Schoen, 1992, p 1). There are also humanitarian and ethical issues involved in managing death within organisations. I would argue that any responsible organisation should attempt to minimise the long-term emotional trauma potentially caused by multiple deaths. This is in line with many arguments which suggest that in order to provide excellent services staff must be treated well (Charles-Edwards, 1992).

There are also some practical consequences of not managing death. I would suggest that ignoring grief and encouraging staff to repress emotion will create problems within the organisation. One is the possible manifestation of other emotions which may be inappropriate, such as anger and resentment. As Charles-Edwards argues, "unresolved loss in one area of our life may make subsequent changes difficult to manage" (Charles-Edwards, 1992, p 3). Schoen's work also noted the effects of ignoring grief in organisations and she suggests

> Unresolved grief often plays a substantial and hidden role in organisational problems such as reduced productivity, low morale, increased conflict, absenteeism, increased turnover, difficulty setting limits and inadequate attention to positive feedback and informal support. (Schoen, 1992, p 2)

It is also apparent that emotions such as anger and blame are expressed where distress is not acknowledged. This concept is discussed by Jaques when he writes, "One example of social mechanisms of defence against

13

paranoid anxieties is that of putting bad internal objects and impulses into particular members of an institution" (Jaques, 1990, p 426), such as, using particular people as scapegoats. Painful feelings are projected onto these scapegoats and are not adequately acknowledged – this process creates painful and difficult to manage group dynamics.

Methodology

My recommendations regarding how organisations should address the issue of multiple bereavements have evolved from three stages of inquiry: first, the exploration of my own experience; second, consideration of views expressed by others in interviews and from publications; and third, the combining of all this information into recommendations for management strategies.

Personal experience

During the last eight years I have worked, and continue to work, as a manager in two organisations dealing with multiple deaths. The first was an organisation providing services to people with AIDS, the second an organisation providing services to people with breast cancer. Both organisations not only provide services to these client groups but they also employ people with these diseases as staff and volunteers.

As I have already mentioned, writing this paper is in itself part of my own processing of grief experienced within these organisations – the use of my personal experience is integral to my objective concerning personal process. Throughout this paper I call upon this professional experience and my experience of deaths in my personal life. Much of my experience I have recorded in a diary, from which I quote in the foreword; this was one of my ways of dealing with the emotions.

Any account of my experience and my perception of the experience of others are in no way intended to make assumptions about the feelings of others. My hope is that my own experience may shed light on the issues that arise and in completing this paper be useful to others. I do not view myself as an objective observer, but as a participant. I have considerable experience, but it is mine. I have beliefs but they are mine; they will, I hope, be useful but not conclusive. Morgan's book, *Beyond method*, discusses many of the issues I encountered in this exploration and I agree with much of what he argues (Morgan, 1983). With regard to truth he writes, "it is necessary to replace the notion that assumptions and knowledge can be certain, authoritative and unambiguously 'true' ... with the idea that uncertainty is the defining feature" (Morgan, 1983, p 383). I find this perspective very helpful as I am sceptical about absolute truths in this arena and do not purport my conclusions from this exploration to be truth. My ideas may or may not feel relevant to others. They may or may not be useful to others. I offer them as an exploration, to open and discuss some questions, to consider answers. I also accept that my sense of reality and fact are mine and are not objective realities. Thus, my background and experiences will have affected my learning. However, I am aware of this potential bias and have attempted to balance it with the use of interviews and other people's research. Reason and Marshall describe this perspective: "if researchers are committed to the pursuit of rigorous critical subjectivity, if they are prepared and able to use their subjectivity as part of the inquiry process, if they have the skills and support to manage and transcend this restimulated distress, the response can be creative and developmental" (Boud and Griffin, 1987, p 115). Thus I hope to arrive at something which is useful to others as well as to myself.

Interviews

For the purpose of this paper I carried out a small number of interviews with four managers who work in organisations which care for the dying. These were carried out in a relatively unstructured way and I recorded the conversations on tape. I simply posed the widest question possible, 'How best should death be managed in organisations?' I was non-directive throughout the interview and based my technique on Rogerian counselling theory (Rogers, 1951). I wanted the conversation to flow in the direction the interviewee thought was most relevant to the issue of managing death. It was important to keep in mind my counselling experience since, inevitably, while discussing death, people experience emotions relating to grief.

I chose not to interview non-managers about their experience of being managed within organisations. This would have been an alternative way of progressing this inquiry but I identified two problems with this. First, to fully explore ways of managing within organisations experiencing multiple deaths directly by asking staff about their experience would have required a lot of data from them which would then have to be cross-referenced with both the style of line management they were receiving and the ethos of the organisation. This would have been fascinating but too time-consuming for my purposes. Second, I would have had to allow the time to deal with the feelings that arose in the interviews of staff who might never have had the opportunity to discuss their experiences of bereavement before.

I do not present these four interviews combined with my personal experience as a representative sample used to produce an objective piece of work. They form four views which I have used to refine and inform my ideas regarding managing death. They both challenge and support my own views. I am able to place this wider selection of perspectives on managing in context because I am familiar with the organisations they come from and the cultures within them. In order to preserve anonymity but also consistency as to perspective I have described them in terms of their roles as Senior Manager, Middle Manager, Charge Nurse and Nurse Educator.

Publications and research

I have read some of the published work in the arenas of loss and change, organisational culture, theories on death and bereavement and other relevant publications. There is an enormous amount written about loss and death, and a good selection on loss and change in organisations. However, there is very little I could find specifically on death and bereavement in organisations and how this should be managed. I have made use of some of the work written on the hospice movement which includes managing staff within such organisations.

My own experience

Motivations

My personal experience of bereavement ranges from the deaths of my father, grandmother, friends, acquaintances, friends' friends and the many deaths I have known in my work. I have experienced death from a variety of perspectives and in a number of different roles – primary carer, daughter, colleague, manager, friend or distant acquaintance.

In developing this paper it is important that I should explore some personal motivations for working in this field. In order to begin to understand others and their relationship to death I must explore my own. I don't believe that my truth is the truth, but in line with my central philosophy of being oneself and that the concept of objectivity is obsolete in this field (Boud and Griffin, 1987), and for the sake of integrity (at the risk of being self-indulgent), I feel I must explore my motivations.

My first experience of a death at work was in my first permanent job. A colleague died in autumn 1987. The thing most remarkable to me about her death was that I felt that she slowly committed suicide in front of us all and we more or less ignored her. She drank alcohol at work all day. I was a clerical officer and a young colleague and I tried to discuss it with her line manager. I felt that she needed help and ignoring this was tantamount to saying that she didn't matter. The manager argued that she did her job adequately and therefore he could do nothing. A friend and I continued to feel concern and discussed it with a senior manager who seemed surprised and concerned and yet apparently did nothing. I left and a few months later she died of liver failure. I'm not sure anything could have been done, but I felt that ignoring her behaviour was not supportive. I think that her death and the attitude of the organisation to it was one of the reasons I became interested in how to deal better with emotions at work.

A further motivation was my experience of my father's death. He didn't have the quality of care from either the health system or from his family that I feel he should have had. Perhaps it was this realisation and the attached guilt that led me to this field of work. However, this highly personal issue is now only a minor motivation. I am now involved in a fascinating and important arena which continues to keep me engaged. I later explore the motivations for people in general, many of which might be true for me to a greater or lesser extent.

I began working at an AIDS organisation in the summer of 1988. HIV was a 'new' disease and this was the first purpose-built project in Britain with the object of providing a full range of services to people 'affected' by HIV. I found joining the organisation a relatively easy decision and now look back at my emotional naiveté with some surprise. I think that I expected to be able to control my feelings and experience of death at some level. Many people suggested I would only 'be able to cope with it' for about two years. I wonder now in what context people can 'cope' with multiple deaths. I see no time limit nor have I learnt a prescribed coping mechanism and what does 'cope' actually mean? It is easy to see when people are not coping but it is difficult to see where the line is drawn. I left the AIDS project in March 1994 and joined an organisation providing services to women with breast cancer.

I have found that the most important motivation for me in working with the dying is in helping them to have the best death they might have, possibly in the hope that one day this will be done for me. I would describe this 'best death' as something about going with the person who is dying, travelling with them towards their death as far as you can go, hopefully thus making the experience less frightening and isolating (though it may also be a way of not letting go – as Stroud writes, "There is a fine line between encouraging the patient to fight the disease and allowing them to let go of their hold on life" [1993, p 176]). This process of letting go is fundamentally important to a peaceful death. Once the business of living is finished and things are resolved, people begin to lose interest in the outside world, they relax and then die. People's ability to carry on living until they have done what they feel they need to, such as, to say good bye to a loved one, or to see someone through something, is very powerful and often when the medical profession expect a death which then takes a long time to come it is because of 'unfinished business'.

My mechanisms for coping

I have developed a number of ways to enable me to 'cope' with the pain of working in an environment where there are many deaths. Boundaries are important; I consciously and, I suspect, subconsciously, limit the amount of close, intimate relationships I have with people who I know are dying. An important distinction for me is whether it is truly a two-way friendship or whether it is a working, though still close relationship.

I know that at any one time I only allow myself to feel close to a couple of people who are very ill. This sort of control is, of course, easier said than done and I will often find myself feeling a lot of pain when I would not have expected to. I seem to have developed a sense of boundaries unconsciously which enable me to continue making contact. These boundaries are far from consistent and fail-safe; however, they do work to an extent.

I also invest a lot of time and energy in my own support. In the past I have attended and facilitated a work support group. This allows time for me to explore why I work in this field, how to deal with the pain and how to allow myself to develop emotionally in the long term in order to continue to work effectively. I have learnt how to ask for support and not to feel guilty about doing so.

Finally, in practical terms, I try to make sure that I have sufficient breaks from work, in terms of holidays, pleasure and gaps in my daily routine. This is sometimes not as successful as I would hope as I can't predict what is going to happen. It is vital for me to regularly get completely away from illness in order to try to regain a perspective that is not dominated by loss and pain, or simply very intense emotion.

The context

It is important to put the concept of managing multiple bereavements in context. Organisations are part of society and their ethos and culture is a product of the individual participants involved in them. These participants or 'stakeholders' include clients, service users or customers, staff, managers, trustees, funders, shareholders and anyone else coming into contact with the organisation. The various cultural contexts and values which contribute to these organisations will affect the organisation's culture regarding death. Organisations cannot be separated from the cultural and societal context in which they are based. Morgan writes, "When we recognise that the individuals, groups and organisations have needs that must be satisfied, attention is invariably drawn to that fact that they depend on a wider environment for various kinds of sustenance" (Morgan, 1986, p 44).

Attitudes and values concerning death differ and how these impact on the organisation's behaviour regarding death will depend fundamentally on two things: first, the relative power and influence of the individual stakeholders; and second, how much the individual's attitudes and values conform with those that dominate society in general. It is impossible to separate the organisation from the society and the issue of death itself is wide and complicated in a sociological or anthropological context. Thus there are layers of influence: the individual; his or her personal culture and values; the organisation; and society.

The prevailing attitudes to death

The study of death and dying is extensive. It affects us all and is one of the areas which sociologists, psychologists and anthropologists explore when studying cultures and societies. Pine says "different social organisations engender different reactions to death-related phenomena" (Pine, 1972, p 150). Thus, when examining death and dying within organisations, it is important that we take into account the social/cultural context of the organisations. Pine describes three levels: that of the individual, the group and the society. For my purposes the organisation is the group level. In order to manage multiple bereavements managers need to understand the processes for the individual and the societal attitudes, despite the fact that they too are members of the society and will be experiencing similar influences. The dominant theories concerning death in society will affect behaviour within organisations since the individuals involved are members of both the wider society and the organisation. They will either experience them as similar values and practices, or they will experience them as differing. Whichever situation is the case I would argue that an impact will be felt upon the individual. Managers need to understand this relationship in order to manage any conflict which might arise. What might seem the best way to manage multiple bereavements within an organisation might be experienced by staff as conflicting with their external experience and expectations. This conflict and social pressure might create a tension for them. This does not mean that organisations should simply follow the line of the dominant culture but that they should at least understand it and work out ways to work with it rather than create conflicts and tensions for staff. For instance, if the organisation encourages staff to discuss feelings that arise for them, this needs to be done with the understanding that this might be difficult given the social context which sometimes sees talking about a death as private, self-indulgent or 'dwelling on it'.

Death has increasingly become a taboo subject in modern English society. The Charge Nurse spoke of "a conspiracy to deny grieving ... and a lot of religious belief simply denies death; that is its function". This taboo has either generated, or is a product of, a social denial of the existence of death. This denial may extend to, or be part of, a denial of the emotional impact of death. Pine argues that

> ... in societies that are organised around bureaucratic structures and highly formal institutions, the impact of death of an individual is considerably diminished no matter how much his loss might mean to the other individuals with whom he interacts on an interpersonal level. (Pine, 1972, p 151)

I define this as a form of denial. The feelings and the effects of the death are denied to people and the expectation is that they will not be affected. Charles-Edwards argues that "Whereas sex was the great taboo for the Victorians, for much of the twentieth century it has been replaced by death" (Charles-Edwards, 1992, p 3). He further argues that the "taboo about death involves avoiding the subject or talking about it as indirectly as possible. Currently, rituals on death in Britain tend to deny reality" (Charles-Edwards, 1992, p 17). This is exemplified by the use of euphemisms for death and the inability of many to talk about it without embarrassment. These shifts were again apparent in an interview with a hospice nurse by Lush in her book about Trinity Hospice. The nurse said that

> ... admitting openly that I have seen death and chose of my own free will to work in its proximity can be quite a shock to some people. For some reason society has regressed in its ability to accept death .... As life expectancy has increased, so has our fear of death. (Lush, 1991, p 32)

Understanding feelings and values relating to death is particularly important for managers given the shift during this century from deaths at home to deaths within institutions. As James states,

> Modern death is more likely to take place in an institution, with health care professionals doing the 'work' formerly carried out by the family and shaping the ways in which predictable emotions associated with death are expressed – or repressed. (James, 1989, p 19)

Sontag writes about "how much harder it has become in advanced industrial societies to come to terms with death" (Sontag, 1991b, p 8).

This is compounded by the fact that in America the death rate has fallen in relation to the birth rate, particularly among the young, which has resulted in "less familiarity with how to cope with it" (Pine, 1972, p 152). Pine also argues that the management of death has been taken up by institutions and 'experts' and has turned into what the Middle Manager described as "a bureaucratic hassle rather than all the emotional things". This has, in some contexts, been taken further, and has been referred to as "the medicalisation of death" (Clark, 1993, p 132). The effect of this shift is the reduction of the general public's contact with death. Pine argues that "participation in funerals is increasingly restricted to family members rather than involving the larger community" (Pine, 1972). This has resulted in "a greater emotional burden than in the past". Death might have become less disruptive to society but "it has become more serious for the bereaved individuals". Pine quotes Blauner (1966) who in his work argued that the bereaved "experiences grief less frequently, but more intensely, since his emotional involvements are not diffused over an entire community, but are usually concentrated on one or a few people" (Pine, 1972, p 152).

Denial and reduced exposure to death in society in general will extend to organisations and in some ways will be compounded. Jaques argues that "institutions are used by their individual members to reinforce defence against anxiety" (Jaques, 1990, p 420). The denial of death could well be perceived as a defence against anxiety, though I believe it to be an inappropriate one.

The role of ritual is believed to be important to the grieving process. Funerals are in some ways the most explicit ritual attached to death. Pine argues that

> Funeral rites allow the bereaved to pass through the period of adjustment following death with a defined social role, ... also provide an occasion for group assembly, reaffirm social values. (Pine, 1972, p 150)

What is interesting about funerals is the similarities between them in most cultures and societies. They clearly perform a social as well as practical function. It is important that their function is understood when managing multiple bereavements. Ritual evolves for a purpose; to undermine this organisationally may well undermine people's ability to grieve.

Given society's attitudes to death and dying there are some organisations which challenge these attitudes directly in their philosophy and ethos. These include some hospices and some organisations working with people with AIDS. They argue that taboos about death should be challenged and that denial is not conducive to healthy bereavement or an easy death. An AIDS organisation had as one of its three objectives 'to work to change the deep-rooted attitudes which deny that death and dying are central to life and living'. Similarly, many hospices argue a need to talk about death. Within the hospice I visited I was told by the Nurse Educator that, "Everybody here knows you can talk to patients about their care openly and there aren't any no-go areas". The potential conflict of values is something managers need to be aware of. As the Nurse Educator said, "There is a conflict because people bring with them their own attitudes and values". If this is recognised and acknowledged by staff and management, conflicts can be addressed when they arise. Staff and management need to be aware of different perspectives on death and to work with the patients and loved ones on their terms, and at their pace, on the process of dying. Thus, the differing values and practices must be flexible and not domineering for either staff or service users.

Theories on grief and bereavement

Managers and staff need to understand not only the attitudes to death in the wider society but also some of the processes which occur in people when someone they know dies. It is useful to explore the key theories about grief and bereavement. This outline gives a perspective which forms some understanding of the grieving process.

One of the leading theorists on the subject of death and dying is Elizabeth Kubler-Ross. Her work with the terminally ill has resulted in the development of a theory about the stages the dying go through when informed of their illness: 'denial and isolation', 'anger', 'bargaining', 'depression' and 'acceptance' (Kubler-Ross, 1970). These, in some ways, might be applied to some of the stages people go through when they are bereaved – the expected loss of one's own life may create similar emotional reactions to the loss of a loved one. Charles-Edwards takes these stages further, however, and explores other emotions which arise in the bereaved: "shock, acute grief, denial, searching, fear, pretence and fantasy, guilt, anger and resentment, loneliness, resolution and acceptance" (Charles-Edwards, 1992).

Another leading theorist on the subject of grief is Colin Murray-Parkes. He has worked in the field of hospices and bereavement studies for many years. He discusses the common perspective of grief as a "mental illness" but he views it more as a "physical injury". The loss may be spoken of as a "blow". As in the case of a physical injury "the 'wound' gradually heals; at least it usually does" (Murray-Parkes, 1986, p 25). He sees bereavement as similar to many other losses we experience in the pattern of emotions we might feel and adds that bereavement as well as being an experience of grief will involve "stigma and deprivation" (Murray-Parkes, 1986, p 28). Grief he describes as a "process of realisation, of 'making real' the fact of loss" (Murray-Parkes, 1986, p 175). Stroud's book about the experience of having cancer (1993) gives an account of the stages of grief. She writes that accepting having cancer and accepting death are separate and that "They may feel shocked and disappointed because the denial, anger, depression or bargaining all flood back again, and have to be faced once more, when death comes closer" (Stroud, 1993, p 169).

Though most of the work on grief refers to private grief, there has been some work done on grief at work. Worden's book, written for bereavement counsellors, recommends three things: "know your own limitations ... practice active grieving ... know how to reach out for help and know where support comes from" (Worden, 1987, p 112). Worden also argues that resolution of past losses is vital if we are to come to terms with new bereavements.

The patterns of grief in individuals is relevant within organisations. I also think we can learn something from grief within families, another group which might apply to managing bereavement within organisations. Worden writes

> Most families exist in some type of homeostatic balance and the loss of a significant person in that family group can unbalance this homeostasis and cause the family to feel pain and to seek help. (Worden, 1987, p 97)

Similarly, there is an equilibrium within organisations which is upset by deaths within them, particularly deaths of staff members which are relatively frequent within self-help, health-related, voluntary organisations. One of the parallels with families particularly apparent to me when working within such organisations is the taking up of certain roles within teams when colleagues die. In my experience someone takes a chief mourner role, someone the carer of others, the manager often takes a parenting role, and so on. The Charge Nurse felt that "because I'm the boss and I'm a woman people expect me to be a bit motherly with them". The role taken at a death might well relate to the role in the team. Another apparent parallel concerns hierarchies within a grieving group. It is likely that the same social pressures apply within teams as within families. Assumptions about appropriate closeness may be made and a hierarchy of grieving occurs. This is a wide generalisation but may be useful when developing strategies to manage bereavement.

A paper I wrote earlier in my degree relates to the issue of death within a team I managed. I observed a process that I was involved in, of the adoption of roles. These roles had parallels to those adopted within family groups. The roles included a parenting one, which as manager I either adopted or was ascribed, a comforter, a practical rationaliser, someone who was angry, and so on. They appeared to form as a result of a number of factors, including structural role within the hierarchy, age, gender and personality. People within the team also took turns in the particular roles. Thus it was a fluid position. This experience was borne out by the Charge Nurse who said,

> Some people are the comforter, others the rescuer and some express all the feelings of the group. Some are seen to own the event in the way others are not. Sometimes in a crisis people snap into old roles; so sometimes they are not acting out of their usual day to day role but they're acting out of an older thing from their childhood, or whatever, when they were a rescuer or something.

Cultures within caring organisations

The importance of the organisation's culture in relation to emotion is explored in Wiley's essay (1990). Wiley argues that "just as reality and the self are constructed and reconstructed through an unending social process of interaction with others and the self, so is feeling", and that "Organisations as groups of interacting individuals create their own cultures which will have a profound effect on how and what emotions are expressed by the individuals involved in the organisation" (Wiley, 1990). Overall I would agree with this hypothesis to the extent that the culture of an organisation will affect the expression of emotion within it. Thus, when managing multiple bereavement within organisations, it is important to consider the culture. As Charles-Edwards writes, "a supportive enabling organisational culture can be more effective in helping staff cope with bereavement that a blaming, punitive one" (Charles-Edwards, 1992, p 14).

There are a number of organisations that deal in particular with death and dying. People die in hospital, in hospices, at home or in residential or nursing homes. On comparing these institutions in terms of stress to staff, James found that in hospitals "stress can be amplified by working conditions and staff divisions", in hospices stress is managed "by team support and agreed goals", at home stress to staff "can be minimal, but late call-in and staff divisions may lead to stress" and in nursing or residential homes stress may "arise from the general working conditions" (James, 1989, p 10). Hospices are particularly interesting when looking at the management of multiple bereavements. They were established to care for the dying in response to what was perceived of as a gap in the care of the terminally ill, particularly those dying of cancer. Other organisations also work regularly with people who are dying, and these include cancer organisations, organisations working with people with HIV and AIDS, residential homes for elderly people and hospitals generally. It is these types of organisation that Schoen identifies as potential arenas for creating what she calls "chronic traumatic stresses" or "loss saturation" (Schoen, 1992, p 1).

It is difficult to generalise about the organisations that primarily work with the dying and their cultures, but with exceptions (particularly large hospitals), I would argue that they do have some similar characteristics which help to define the arena in which managers will be dealing with multiple bereavements. On the whole, they are medium-sized organisations with a paid staff of approximately 100, most of whom are nurses or care assistants, with some volunteers. They will usually have budgets of between £1m and £10m and may be registered charities. All the organisations I have considered within this inquiry have hierarchies based on a pyramid type structure.

Often the stated purpose, with the exception of hospices, will not be to care for the dying, but will be more general and will include the care and support of all affected by the illness. They are also likely to have what is perceived of as a holistic approach; "a seamless web of care" (Lush, 1991, p 29) is provided. The care can range from the conventional medical and psycho-social approaches to a number of complementary services. Hospices often also specify staff support as a factor in their philosophy. One London hospice's 'Philosophy of Care' includes a statement that "Support for staff is provided both by appropriate management structures and informally through the operation of the interdisciplinary team".

Many of the organisations which care for the ill and dying will have a stated ethos and model of care. This will affect not only the experience of those who are using the services of the organisations but all those who work within them. The experience of dying and working with the dying in an NHS hospital will be different to that of dying or working in an organisation which consciously addresses the issues relating to death. The traditional approach to nursing care emphasised being 'professional' and not getting attached to patients; however, some hospices and similar organisations encourage closer contact. There are some overlaps in both these approaches, and this was evident in the interview I carried out with a Charge Nurse who had come from the NHS. She argued

> You are employed to do a job and that job is to provide some objectivity to people who are probably saturated with emotion from their own families and the last thing anybody needs is a wailing health care worker who is having problems with their feelings.

These organisations are also likely to be environments in which people feel a sense of ownership and belonging. As Vachon argues, for some, the "hospice becomes a major part of their life and identity". This is partly because the culture and ethos is very defined. James, in her work, argues that in hospices the ethos is often of "total care" and "highlights the point that social, spiritual and psychological difficulties require management and attention in the same way that physical symptoms do" (James, 1989, p 20). Thus, nurses that are providing these services will need management and supervision which relates to all the aspects of the care that they provide.

Another aspect of the culture is the issue of how the client or patient is perceived. Often the ethos will be one of empowerment and patient choice. The organisations will encourage the patients to be informed about their situation and for a high level of openness to be present. This raises many issues and is part of the overall movement for more openness in health care generally. This is explored fully in Faulder's book on 'informed consent' (Faulder, 1985). What is important to consider in this context is how this affects staff. Honesty can feel both liberating and a burden. The position of keeping bad news from 'patients' may well have been partly to protect the patients; however, it could also allow the carer to avoid difficult emotional issues. But the question is, does it really? I would argue that the ability to be honest is usually liberating and often people will know the truth but will be colluding with one another about their denial of it.

Many organisations that address cancer or HIV have grown from self-help groups and involve staff who have been affected by the disease. This can mean that many of the deaths are from within the organisation and in my experience deaths among staff are often the most difficult to bear. The founder of BACUP (a cancer organisation), Vicky Clement-Jones, had ovarian cancer herself and died in 1987. When she died the organisation reeled from the experience and as Faulder wrote in her book, "The anticipation of loss bore no resemblance to the reality ... the ship juddered and creaked at it plunged through some very heavy seas" (Faulder, 1991, p 207). It is important that such organisations are equipped to deal with the impact of deaths.

The interviews I carried out included people from three different organisations. Two had very explicit philosophies about death – the hospice and the HIV organisation. As the Charge Nurse said, "the big number here is that it is emotionally healthy to talk about death and accept death and accept that you will die and grieve openly about people. That's the rhetoric but not what is allowed in reality". The breast cancer organisation does not mention death explicitly. This was evident in the interview in that the interviewee was unwilling even to use the word 'death', though she did explore the issue of patients and staff all colluding around the taboo about death.

These characteristics of culture I have mentioned – the size, structure, explicit philosophies, explicit ethos or philosophy and the models of care, perception of the client or patient, the self-help element, and the employment of staff and volunteers with the disease – are all factors which need to be considered in the context of managing multiple bereavements within organisations.

Change and loss in organisations

There has been a considerable amount written on loss and change in organisations, usually relating to the implementation of change and how managers might facilitate this process. The issue of change and its effect on organisations is useful in the context of bereavement within organisations, as grief and loss are essentially about change. Some of the stages that people pass through during organisational upheaval will have similarities to reactions people have when they experience a bereavement.

A number of models have been developed to explain emotions people experience in a climate of loss and change which show emotions set against a time-scale. One such model describes a series of stages: "freezing, minimising, depression – slumping, accepting the realities, testing and finally emerging". Another outlined by a previous tutor describes the process as a journey along a river including "swimming upstream, clinging to the banks, shooting the rapids and navigating the way". These models can provide a structure and show emotional reaction to change as a process, thus giving us assurance of progressive improvement when in emotional pain.

These models also apply to organisations that care for the dying. They may exhibit even more extreme reactions to the usual changes, or unpredictable losses within organisations. The Nurse Educator in the hospice told me how an unexpected death "had an enormous impact on the organisation ... a big funeral with hundreds of people and a commemorative tree and the students set up a trust fund to have an annual lecture". Similarly, they may exhibit more extreme reactions with regard to structural or political change within organisations.

A consistent issue in the organisations that care for the dying which is of interest to me is that of the role of power and how the management is perceived. The Charge Nurse I interviewed said

> ... a lot of individual pain and grief gets converted into anger or sabotage. People say "you're making us do this work and you're not supporting us". Quite often when I get angry here it will be a time when I'm going through grief ... when I'm feeling vulnerable and powerless ... I

could leap at the wrong phrase in a job description like it was a war crime.

I found similarities in the breast cancer organisation. When dealing so directly with death the stakes get raised and any heavy-handed management feels more brutal. This was commented upon in the interview with the Senior Manager when we discussed an outside consultant who

> ... drew an allegory of this organisation (during a time of upheaval); what somebody was trying to do was to sort of cut the cancer out; we had a whole and what they perceived as bad was in one place and they were trying to cut this out ... it mirrored cancer, because in fact we all behaved like organisms that were behaving in strange ways.

The Senior Manager went on to say she felt that the organisation still needed to heal. She was still using the disease imagery to discuss the organisation.

Managers should be aware of the high level of vulnerability and emotional tensions which arise in this sort of environment. As the Charge Nurse said,

> ... there isn't really an understanding of how much loss and change and unpredictability and lack of control people are facing all the time, how they are drenched in that already and that if things happen here suddenly, unpredictability without explanation and consultation it is too much .... It is possible to aim to manage change well ... to aim to inform and consult people and where possible to keep the pace manageable. To not move faster than necessary ... It's common sense, if something rubs in the same place all the time it will hurt. If we keep putting more change on more change then the bottom drops out, we just wear on the same spot.

Contributing Factors

To me it's almost like a landscape or a place, loss. I just think, I'm in that landscape again, I'm in that place again, that's what it feels like to me. Where my perception is slightly altered and my appetite has gone, my temper's short and I can't engage, I'm behind a glass wall. When I get there again it always shocks me. It's like a recurring nightmare. It's a place I go back to. Now I recognise it earlier, I stay less long and I'm more able to get out of it. It's got parallels with hill or mountain walking. There are things you do if you get lost. If you get lost don't just wander, because if you wander from the first place ... the other territory is not so safe. You might have only been half a mile away .... I wander less now when I'm in that landscape. I know what will work for me .... I don't force myself to eat, I get up if I can't sleep, have plenty of books and talk to people. That's the kind of stuff you can't inject into people but if we had more structured ways to consider how loss and grief feels and how we deal with it we could help each other more than we do .... People are more alone with their grief than they need to be. (Middle Manager)

The previous chapter established the context in which managers are likely to be managing multiple bereavements, both ideologically and practically. There are also a number of further issues and factors worth considering which contribute to an understanding of the context we are working in. These include questions regarding what motivates people to work in this field, what emotions are engendered by such work and what other factors might contribute to the bereavements and their manageability. Having explored some of the answers to these questions and contextualised the issue it is possible to develop some strategies and recommendations for best practice when managing multiple or cumulative bereavements.

It is possible and sensible to make employees' experience of multiple bereavements more bearable. Marris (1986) argues that

> ... recovery from bereavement varies with the circumstances of loss, the nature of the loss and the past history of the bereaved .... Vulnerability to depression seems to be

influenced by a very similar combination of factors. (Marris, 1986, p xiii)

However, we need to acknowledge our own limitations as managers and the limit of our responsibilities. It was put simply by the Middle Manager who said "If you raise people's expectations they expect too much". My own experience confirms this – if you say to people that you will provide support for their emotional well-being they expect to feel happy all the time at work; of course, this is not possible.

Careful consideration given to the management of bereavement needs to be a conscious process on the managers' behalf. It is easy to see how damaging it can be to staff to ignore their stress and to allow repeated burnout to occur. However, it is also important to consider what damage can be done by inappropriate management of multiple bereavements. Collusion with what might be inappropriate emotional reactions, projection of feelings towards the wrong subject or encouraging people to dwell on distress will not result in best practice. As put by the Middle Manager, "You can get collusion in abnormal or prolonged grief in a culture that actually sets out to support people". Thus the right balance is not easy to find.

Staff motivation

Why do people choose to work with the dying? I have briefly discussed my own motivations earlier, and I have witnessed a wide range of motivations in others. There have been occasions where I have considered people's motivations inappropriate, such as a particularly evangelical religious stance. On one such occasion the prospective staff member believed they could "help people die" in a specific way. It is also important to know if people choose to work in the field because of their own emotional needs. I would not argue that this means that they should not be involved with the organisation but I consider it useful for the manager to know what their experience has been and whether they feel able to deal with the experience of working with the dying given their personal experience.

My views were borne out by the Charge Nurse I interviewed who said that she included questions about why people chose to work in the HIV field in the recruitment process. She argued that it was important to "Recognise why people choose to work in areas where they know there will be many deaths" and that "Their needs will be different and therefore how you manage that will be different". She was clear:

> It's about where people are, what they've come into the organisation to do, what their experience has been, where they are in terms of their exposure to grief or loss and then supporting them on an ongoing basis through that .... If you are consciously employing somebody who has had a recent bereavement and who is expressing difficulties of coping with it in the interview then you can bet your bottom dollar they are coming here to work on the issue, and what you can do is ask yourself can I manage this at the moment, which is about looking at your skill mix.

This view is also evident in Vachon's work, where she argues that a "balanced team", or skill mix, is necessary in order for people to manage stress when working with the dying. In terms of personality, Vachon believes hospices need

> ... people who have enough personal maturity, outside interests and a deep enough personal philosophy .... This implies a level of insight into one's own personal needs and motivation and an understanding of when it's time to move on.

There seems to be another category of person who chooses to work in this area. They were defined by the Charge Nurse as "death junkies". She felt that there were people who almost indulged themselves in the emotional drama of death and were in some ways addicted to the process. "I think it is an addiction to a kind of intensity and the other thing it might be is unresolved loss and grief people have." Vachon discusses this category of people, who she refers to as "intensity vultures who required the high which comes with the constant association of dealing with crises of life and death". She further felt that "The intimacy that you have with people before they die can be incredibly rewarding. There is no way you can do that and not pine for it, and some people come for the growth and development that they feel they can get from working at the edge of something".

Vachon's study on why people choose to work with the dying found

> Many came into this field with a sense of purpose and commitment borne out of personal experience with death, a sense of disenchantment with the dehumanisation of the dying person within the hospital setting and a desire to avoid the use of technology in prolonging the dying process by focusing on quality of life as opposed to quantity of life.

These findings are in line with my own experience. She also explores other motivations such as "low sense of self esteem", "unmet dependency needs", and the need to give "the care one wishes one had received oneself". She also believes that people are attracted to "a nurturing environment" for the sake of their emotional needs.

An awareness of motivations gives managers the ability to make decisions about how best to address the situation. As the Charge Nurse said, there is something exploitative of the dying in using the experience of their death to process other losses of one's own. I fully understood her when she said "That's when it can feel that you're weeping for a particular person and other people are abusing your loss; they're kind of on the bandwagon ... whose death is it?" I would not suggest that people can define their emotions in such a way as not to allow past feelings to spill into the present, but this should not be a central purpose of their involvement in the organisation.

Emotions engendered

As I have discussed earlier, it is not viable to try to divorce emotions from work. In order to manage staff in such an environment managers must acknowledge that emotions will arise as a result of working with the dying. These emotions will vary from person to person. Menzies Lyth writes about the work of nursing: "The work arouses strong and conflicting feelings: pity, compassion and love; guilt and anxiety; hatred and resentment of the patients who arouse the feelings; envy of the care they receive" (Menzies Lyth, 1990, p 441).

My experience, reading and interviews have highlighted many emotions. One of the prominent ones is of guilt, often manifested when comparing one's own health with the dying. The Senior Manager I spoke to discussed "how it feels to be the well ones ... I have sat in so many rooms where I am the only person with two of her breasts". Within the field of AIDS many people I have met have felt unreasonably lucky in not having contracted HIV.

One of the effects which seems common, and is borne out by my own experience, is that exposure to death makes one more conscious of one's own mortality. As the Nurse Educator put it, "Working with people who are dying, if you are doing it with any degree of success, means you are thinking about your own mortality more than is perhaps the social norm". Gittens found in an interview with a doctor in a hospice "that there is only one certain thing in life, and that's that one day your life will end. I believe that we should try to pack as much into life as possible and make every day count" (Gittens, 1991, p 58). My experience in the field of working with the dying has led me to feeling a sense of urgency. It is not so much about quantity but about quality, a feeling that I will die, and that that will be all right, but that I must live life as I choose, not make too many fundamental compromises and get as much as I can from life. This has definitely affected my day-to-day life in that I do not agree to do things I don't want to, particularly social things, and I am more assertive. 'Life's too short' has a profound resonance. The issue of our own mortality came up in other interviews too. The Senior Manager said "you feel why haven't I got this, then you're terrified someone is going to smite you down". However, she also added, "I plan to die in my late nineties, skiing down a slope and going over". The Charge Nurse I interviewed also spoke of stress and fear: "You suddenly find yourself going home and looking at a spot and thinking 'shit it's a purple spot' [KS, a form of cancer]. Suddenly all reason goes out the window". This example is borne out by the discussion in the hospice, with the Nurse Educator who said,

> I think there is an element of what Kubler-Ross would call 'bargaining' .... I don't think anybody can come to terms with their own mortality so there is probably a calculation and that will be part of the process of distancing yourself from your own death and maybe to a degree from the patient's.

Anger also plays an important role and will often be manifested in inappropriate ways. Vachon considers whether people who choose this work use "warmth and loving as a veneer which covers a controlling personality and a considerable amount of repressed anger". This anger also becomes apparent in the internal politics of the organisation. As I illustrated earlier, feelings become strong and the stakes feel high.

Alternatively, what might be an excessive sense of commitment bordering on bravery and martyrdom can be apparent. However, this can be outweighed by a sense of privilege at being part of something which feels so profoundly important.

Other emotions might include love, depression, sadness, fear, jealousy, shock, denial, isolation and sometimes regression into earlier patterns of behaviour. All these emotions will affect relationships outside work as well as interpersonal dynamics within work. As the Middle Manager said, staff "may go out to the pub more often or bore the pants off their partner talking about work". Managers need to bear in mind some of the likely emotions if they are to manage effectively and efficiently.

Self-identification and professionalism

There are a number of things which contribute to the emotional trauma staff may feel when experiencing death and bereavement at work. In order to manage the situation well, managers must consider these, and where possible, alleviate the negative factors. It might be possible to take these factors into account when planning services or allocating particular staff to working with the dying.

One of the factors which affects people's reaction to a death is how much they identify with the client. The more similar they feel to the client, the more pain they usually experience. This is particularly the case regarding the age of the client. Many people seem to experience increased emotional trauma when the client is young, or their own age. Other factors which affect self-identification are role within a family, such as being a parent; gender; race; and sexuality.

The client's feelings about their own death or about the treatment they have received can also contribute to the worker's experience. If the workers have felt able to provide the client with as much of what they wished for as they could, they are more likely to be able to accept the death. If they feel guilty or sad for the client they are more likely to suffer stress from the death.

One of the other important factors which seems evident is the professional background of staff. Different professions and training have different philosophies and ethos' which affect how the patients are perceived, which in turn affect how they are felt about when they die. This was evident in the interviews. The Charge Nurse said, "You might be getting different answers if you were talking to somebody who wasn't a nurse". Coleman et al (1990) explore this in the context of resettlement and develop a model which is also useful. They identify four models, or approaches: 'personal-physical care', such as nursing or medicine which perceives the client as 'dependent'; 'social care', which might be the counsellor or social worker and perceives the client as 'inter-dependent'; 'practical assistance', which will include information and advice workers and sees the client as 'independent'; and 'advocacy' which also sees the client as 'independent' (Coleman, 1990, p 29).

These different approaches are also evident in the health care of the dying, as often the organisations have a holistic approach and employ a range of professions to provide services in multi-disciplinary teams. This was reflected in the interviews I carried out. The Charge Nurse felt that boundaries were vital. The Middle Manager, a social worker, showed much more expectation of the boundaries being less defined and thought that feelings would be brought to work. "It's about recognising things are difficult for that person at the time and giving them a bit of space and permission to be less capable, or more short-tempered, or whatever". Doctors, who I have not included in my interviews, also provide a different professional perspective. Dowling and Barrett, in their work on doctors during their first year of work after registration, quote a ward sister who said "Consultants are very bad at looking after their own staff. Compared with my work with nurses, I have been trained in this and I expect to give my nurses support. I really resent having to fill the vacuum left by the consultants in this area" (Dowling and Barrett, 1991, p 71). Clear boundaries which identify the client as dependent and/or detached create different reactions to loss than less clear boundaries and the view of an interdependent client. Deciding which is the 'best' approach is in some ways irrelevant. What is important, as a manager, is to understand the professional backgrounds of staff and the potential effects these may have.

Management strategies

Having established a context, and taking into account the two principles that work must be seen in the context of our overall lives and that emotions must be a consideration of management, there are a number of ways I would recommend that organisations and managers facilitate and enable staff to deal well with multiple bereavements. There is no one way which is right for all, but there are a number of strategies that we can undertake to manage multiple bereavements and which lead to better practice in this arena.

Context and theory

One of the factors that is vital for managers when working with staff who care for the dying concerns knowledge. A contextualised and theoretical understanding of bereavement should be any manager's priority when considering a management strategy for multiple bereavement. Understanding the social and cultural context in which death and grief is played out in our society allows us to make appropriate responses to staff and to more fully understand their behaviour and to possibly predict reactions. Further, it allows us to develop strategies to deal with the effects of multiple bereavements proactively. There are also theories regarding grief and bereavement which provide us with useful insight. This insight will allow us to understand and sometimes to predict likely behaviour. This foresight makes practical plans for the impact of deaths viable.

Self-awareness

Understanding the emotional reactions of others is clearly vital in managing staff experiencing multiple bereavements. However, this must also apply to ourselves. Unless we understand our own reactions to deaths we are unlikely to truly understand the reaction of others. We are also unable to have the self-awareness necessary in order to perceive how our reactions affect others. The Charge Nurse put this to me in a converse way when she said "if you don't feel capable of helping with the feelings of others, you don't want to stir them up ... then what are you doing with your own feelings?" It works in both directions: an understanding of our own feelings, self awareness, is a pre-requisite for understanding the feelings of others. This is in keeping with the theories concerning counselling and therapy.

Recruitment and training

An early opportunity we have, as managers, to address the issue of the management of grief is in the selection process. It was suggested by the Charge Nurse I interviewed that at the recruitment stage we should ask questions about grief and "see how people respond at interview stage to see what awareness and insight they've got". This was borne out by the Nurse Educator at the hospice who said, "we would inquire of people about their personal experience of bereavement". It is sensible to inquire about previous experience of death and how the interviewee managed the loss, to be aware of "residual grief from another source still to resolve" (Charles-Edwards, 1992, p 8). Vachon writes

> Particular attention should be paid to the coping mechanisms the individual employs; evidence of denial of grief or flight into over-activity may be indicative of unresolved grief, which could lead to later difficulty in care for the dying. (Corr and Corr, 1983, p 242)

I think it is important to stress that there is not a right answer to questions on how an interviewee managed deaths previously. However, if they have not in any way 'processed' the loss, there is a likelihood that this is why they have chosen to join the organisation as they may well be searching for an opportunity to resolve the grief. This may be unacceptable, but there may be cases where given the skills you are looking for you have to accept it. However, an awareness of the problems will allow you to build into the new employee's induction and training some work on this.

Induction and training programmes are also important in preparing people for bereavements. It is helpful for people to be given the opportunity to discuss death and the grieving process so that when they experience some of the feelings themselves they have a reference point to work from. These training opportunities should be ongoing and should include all staff and managers. They provide an opportunity for people to learn from one another about coping mechanisms which have proved useful and to nurture mutual support systems. The importance of training was reiterated by the Charge Nurse, who said

> We don't give people enough resources and information about grief and bereavement. This means the first few

losses are a great shock and we're reinventing the wheel all the time. A little further in we should have training days about grieving patterns, about guilt, anger and shame ... we also should tell people physical facts about someone dying so death is not an awful shock. You can't have someone's experience but you can help them prepare.

Or, as the Senior Manager put it,

... if you don't know what the behaviour is then how can you look out for it and understand that it is a reflection of grief ... it's easy when somebody is crying ... but because it manifests itself in other ways and we don't talk about it then it is very difficult to manage it and we need to start talking about it.

It is possible to train staff on the symptoms and effects of stress in order for them to recognise feelings in themselves, and thus reduce fear. Further training on stress management and work on establishing one's own support systems should occur throughout the employment. The Nurse Educator felt that

... there ought to be built into that process an opportunity for people to address those issues and keep returning to them because I don't think they are issues you sort out once. What you think about death and dying is going to change as time goes on and is going to change according to your own experience.

Freedom to express emotion

One of the most important things of all when managing organisations dealing with multiple deaths is to allow people to be themselves and to express their emotions. Marris suggests that "To reconstitute purposes and meaning out of the conflicted and bitter emotions of bereavement, the grief stricken must take charge of the process of their recovery" (Marris, 1986, p xiii). This may sound both simple and impossible. It is also slightly contradictory when discussing strategies for managing bereavement. It might be argued that people must, of course, be allowed to be themselves and to express their emotions. To do otherwise would be very oppressive. Others might suggest that this is impossible, that it would lead to chaos and confusion and that free emotions with no constraints or order would be impossible to manage and thus lead to increased unnecessary distress. Like James, I believe "The repression of emotional expression may appear to lead to greater efficiency in production, but it does not mean the emotions disappear, merely ... that they are concealed" (James, 1989, p 29). The Senior Manager confirmed the need to allow expression:

> We can't deny the feelings, nobody's going to wave a magic wand and say this person is going to live, you're not going to feel terrible pain. But by talking about them we know that other people feel them which makes us feel less isolated; we can cope better.

Having said this I would go further. I believe that much of the trauma associated with work stress and burnout is related to the suppression of feelings. This can lead to absence from work or abuse of clients or patients. I would suggest that at work generally and specifically when dealing with highly emotionally charged arenas people should not only be allowed to express themselves freely, but should be positively encouraged to do so. The organisation and its managers should trust the people involved to express their feelings responsibly, and in my experience they will. An organisation can make it explicit in documentation that members of the organisation may express the feelings which arise when people die. This means trust among members of the organisation, including management, but I would suggest that this trust be bestowed.

The ethos which allows people to express feelings is probably the most important thing to remember when managing staff in this context. The experience of death is highly personal and how people process their loss and what belief systems and values they have, are their own. Managers should respect this. However, my argument concerning the management of organisations dealing with multiple deaths contains a contradiction. I argue that individuals should be allowed and enabled to deal with death as they choose, while I offer suggestions as to how I think they can best do this. This contradiction is explored by Torbert when he writes about "liberating structures ... that cultivate empowerment through development" (Torbert, 1991, p 98). Torbert is referring to the development of management, but this is similar to the contradiction of empowering people to express feeling in a structured way, thus creating a sense of freedom in an environment which has a conscious policy regarding the freedom. Within the context of encouraging expression of feelings among staff there are ways I have found of increasing our ability to deal with, or process, the deaths. What

I am proposing is to allow staff to express their feelings of grief in order to enable them to carry on working.

Challenge denial and acknowledge grief

Death is a part of life; all human beings die. Though there is controversy about what happens after we die there is little disagreement about whether we die. However, this society like others, while acknowledging death on one hand denies it on the other. There are a number of structural ways for denying death, such as some religious stances. More importantly, there are many emotional ways humans use to deny death. Examples of these range from delusions of immortality to dangerous risk taking or even physical self-abuse. More subtly, there is simply many people's semi-conscious belief that they will not die, or their refusal to allow themselves to contemplate the reality. Even, and perhaps in some ways more so, in organisations which experience multiple death people do not truly believe they will die.

Much of the denial that exists is about denying feelings relating to grief rather than literally denying the death. As the Charge Nurse said, "I don't know if there is organisational denial of death but there is denial of how shitty and painful it is and there is the idea of a good death". As the Nurse Educator put it, "It's not damaging to talk about illness and death and dying and to acknowledge that someone has an illness from which they are not going to be cured". I would make the suggestion that the opposite is damaging and disabling. I agree with Owens and Naylor when they say "there are many reasons for believing that regarding death as a taboo subject has been counter-productive" (Owens and Naylor, 1989, p 101), and as the Charge Nurse said, "if you don't recognise the death then you are not giving permission to grieve".

Our continued denial of our own mortality and our suppression of our fear is more stressful and exhausting than our acceptance of death as a reality for all of us. I am not suggesting that it is something we should embrace or celebrate; on the contrary, death is undesirable. However, it is unavoidable. Like existence or gravity it is something there is little point in trying to defy. A ball thrown into the air will fall towards the centre of gravity and though we could choose to use all our energy to keep it in the air it will always keep responding to its gravitational pull. Death is similar in some ways. We may try to avoid death, and this is a natural human reaction; however, we should not try to pretend it doesn't exist and attribute the concept of choice to dying.

In the context of an organisation, denying death can be an excessively exhausting and demoralising process. It is demoralising because losing a fight is painful and can lead to feelings of failure or guilt, both of which are inappropriate and damaging to people working with multiple deaths. Sontag's work on illness (1991b) also brings up the issue of the denial. She writes about the way illness is used as a metaphor and says this is not helpful to us. "My point is that illness is not a metaphor, and the most truthful way of regarding illness – and the healthiest way of being ill – is one most purified of, most resistant to, metaphoric thinking" (Sontag, 1991b, p 3). Her argument that illness should be seen squarely on for what it is, rather than askew, is useful in this context as it is relevant to organisations dealing with illness and dying and has parallels with how death is perceived.

I believe honesty and openness are liberating and enabling when working with the dying. They allow us to express ourselves and to share the responsibility and the burden. I agree with the Nurse Educator who said

> I automatically assume that honesty is a good thing .... I think what happens to people who are dishonest is that they lose their sense of integrity. They feel quite rightly that they are short changing other people by being dishonest and they feel bad about themselves and their work and they get angry about it too.

Levine, who has written a number of books about dying, writes "You are with one who is dying in the same way you are with yourself. Open, honest and caring.... Just hear the truth that the moment has to offer" (Levine, 1988, p 157). There has been a myth that secrecy protects the patient and makes life easier for the carer. However, "exchange, information, respect for one another and the sharing of tasks in an atmosphere of reciprocity" (Guex, 1994, p 77) is what allows sustained exposure to multiple deaths. Without this, the burden of what to tell and what not to tell, the shock of realisation when denial has been effective and the confusion and anxiety of who knows what and what the patient really wants to know is a cause of stress. Or, as put by the Middle Manager "it's very important that people are able to acknowledge what is happening to them in terms of the loss they are experiencing". Our energy should be used on living and not denying dying. The emotions attached to the denial of something which is inevitable are counter to those which help us to have healthy emotional lives. These emotions include a sense of failure, a sense of being wrong, guilt, unexplained anger or pain, and misguided blame. Our sense of failure will arise from something happening, a death which we do not accept as inevitable. We will feel failures because we are proved wrong by death and because we might believe death is preventable by ourselves. Our sense of guilt might be related to this. We might feel that we could have stopped someone dying and that if we had tried harder we could have stopped death happening. We might further believe that some other nurse, doctor, counsellor, friend, relative or partner could have done better, could have saved the person from dying. I appreciate that in a literal sense this might be true. It can be our fault that people die when they do, in an accident or when the wrong drug or dosage is administered. While these things can be our fault, what is not our fault is that people do die. When people can accept death as inevitable then one can reject unnecessary blame, guilt or an unnecessary sense of failure.

Other emotions, such as anger, pain and misguided blame, can also be a result of denial of death. We can become angry with others for their action or inaction and blame them for the person's death. We might feel pain as a result of any of these feelings of guilt, blame and anger. I am not for a moment arguing that death could or should be an emotionless occasion, or that there is a 'right' emotion. I would argue that it is highly emotional and that people will always have strong feelings about it. However, they will not be able to fully process, or come to terms with emotions which are inappropriate. Emotions which are based on not accepting death's existence will not allow the healthier emotional reactions to surface, all of which might be quite similar. These need to be allowed to surface in order for the person to continue to work in an environment containing multiple deaths. Schoen argues that "Acknowledgement of loss reminds staff that there are external sources of distress and minimizes the tendency of staff to blame themselves, others, or the organization for this distress" (Schoen, 1992, p 3).

A further stage of the acceptance of death for others, but directly related, is the acceptance of one's own mortality. If people are working in an environment where they witness many deaths they will inevitably be reminded of their own mortality. If they are constantly trying to develop mechanisms for denying their own mortality they will be suppressing feelings. Again I would argue that this is stressful and exhausting and in the long term not sustainable. Fear of one's own death is a natural and necessary emotion but pretending we won't die is not. The stress resulting from this suppression of fear contributes to the burnout often experienced in this sort of environment.

One of the things we should do for one another is to acknowledge deaths, openly and regularly. This allows opportunity for the expression of feeling and validates the feelings of the bereaved. Many organisations have ways of symbolising deaths within them, such as a candle burning, a name put up on the wall or flowers. This forms a way of communicating the loss to all.

Having said this I would not argue that denial has no function. I think we allow ourselves to absorb things gradually and that there is a level at which we use denial to manage shock. The Senior Manager said "in a way we do need some armour, we can't be total jellies all the time, we won't be able to function, but how do you decide what is healthy defence and what is denial?" We should also respect privacy. I think it is vital that managers bear in mind the importance of denial and do not challenge denial mechanisms without thought. It is possible to allow people to absorb loss gradually without colluding with denial.

The role of ritual

As I have discussed earlier, ritual has played an important role in societies' management of death. Funerals, religious beliefs and functions, social expectations and unwritten rules all provide a ritualistic framework for us to work within. As Charles-Edwards writes, "Religious ritual provides a social structure for support and mourning" (Charles-Edwards, 1992, p 21). Murray-Parkes (1986) argues that it has a psychological value for the bereaved.

> Belief and rituals which provide an explanation for death
> and social support for the expression of grief should reduce
> the confusion felt by helping the newly bereaved and might
> even be of psychological value in helping them express their
> grief. (Murray-Parkes, 1986, p 178)

If ritual has an important role in the management of grief in the wider society it may well have an important function within organisations. The role of ritual is important in providing us with another management strategy for multiple bereavement. The organisations I have worked with have a tendency to encourage staff to attend funerals where possible. The Nurse Educator said "it's much more likely that nurses from the hospice will attend a funeral or memorial service than in my experience in hospitals where patients die and there is very little contact

46

with people afterwards". When I was managing a team the organisation hired a minibus to go to the funeral of a colleague at the expense of the organisation. It is important that the policies state attendance at funerals is to be encouraged where people wish to attend as this helps in the processing of loss and therefore will, in the long run, create less stressed staff. Organisations can also develop their own rituals, such as books of remembrance, or candles burning for those who have died.

Boundaries

Boundaries, particularly boundaries with regard to professionalism and personal relationships, are an issue which create debate in this sphere. Often managers argue that clear boundaries are what provide the safety to enable people to work in a stressful environment. It is also important to consider people's overall lives. The Nurse Educator felt

> The whole issue of boundaries is very important. Success will be reflected outside, it will certainly lie partly in people's ability to have an external life outside the hospice, if they don't have this they are in serious danger of being overwhelmed by the place.

The Charge Nurse said "you can manage it by giving people boundaries and structures and that is about their role and also boundaries in terms of personal involvement". She added later, "it's about people's awareness of what they are doing and boundaries. You can't support people to manage death if what you are saying to them is be vulnerable, totally open yourself up". This is familiar in the field of nursing as a way of dealing with the stress of the work. Whether or not it works, or how much it works is contentious. Hospices differ. As the Nurse Educator said,

> ... we do I think encourage people to go beyond the traditional boundaries and I certainly think this idea that you have to switch off from work and not think about it when you've left is completely unrealistic and I think that would be encouraging people to use avoidance and defensive mechanisms .... But I think that keeping the sort of detachment where you can say to yourself "well I've done what I can today and I'll be back tomorrow to do more", is best.

Another thing managers should take into account is at what stage staff come into contact with the dying. Traditional nursing advocated a level of detachment which would lead to lowered stress levels. Menzies Lyth writes, "The entrant into any profession that works with people needs to develop adequate professional detachment" (1990). However, she goes on to write that this is a form of denial which is "reinforced by the denial of the disturbed feelings that arose within relationships" (Menzies Lyth, 1990, p 445). Fineman refers to this concept as "the bureaucratization of feeling rules" (Fineman, 1993, p 19).

Managing levels of attachment is often possible. Dying in organisations that deal with death, such as hospitals and hospices, is often quite a predictable process. People may have conditions which are terminal and their death will not be a shock to staff. In this context I have found it is easier for staff to deal with the death when they have been involved with the patient or client during a reasonably long time. Even though the length of contact will bear a relation to the immediate level of emotional reaction to loss, longer contact will be more endurable. To be involved with large numbers at their final hours will give a skewed perspective on their deaths. Whereas, if a member of staff has watched the gradual deterioration of the patient and has had a role in improving their quality of life and possibly even witnessed the patient's acceptance of their own death, they will be more likely to put it in a perspective that is tolerable, and may have had "time to prepare" (Charles-Edwards, 1992, p 23). As the Nurse Educator put it, "I think intuitively with human beings, if there is a relationship with a degree of continuity, there is likely to be an increasing amount of trust on both sides". However, I found that others did not agree. The Middle Manager felt "it's usually about seeing people change over time, knowing their families, being aware of things in their life that can cause emotional trauma". She suggested there was yet another perspective when she added, "People who are exposed to people in short bursts might be dealing with the magnitude of that ... overwhelmed by the numbers rather than the intensity", and further suggested that there were advantages in what she described "as being able to do things all the way through and put them in the fridge. What it does mean is that it will be a complete bereavement. You will have been able to say good-bye and you will have finished your business".

This issue is closely related to the previous suggestion that death is a part of life which we should accept along with our own mortality. If this is the case, when one is experiencing the death of a patient one can put it into the context of both life and death for all of us, and in the context of this particular individual's process of living and dying.

Mutual support

One of the issues which managers should consider is the sense of community within the organisations concerned, and the role of mutual support among staff. This can be built directly into the care of the dying. As Vachon writes,

> One of the most effective ways to decrease staff stress is through the use of a well-organised multi-disciplinary team approach to the care of patients. Communication between staff members is enhanced, responsibility is more effectively shared, and no one feels totally alone in caring for the patient, staff cooperation and effectiveness are usually increased. (Corr and Corr, 1983, p 244)

I have certainly felt that there is a contact between staff members which is not necessarily felt in other organisations, perhaps a feeling of struggling together in an environment of pain and trauma, and a feeling of mutual understanding within a group which others outside the community could not understand. This again brings up the issue of 'family' in organisations. Vachon argues there is a need for work on whether workers in hospices begin to behave like families and she considers the issue of roles such as the 'rebellious adolescent'. As I have mentioned earlier, I have found in my own experience that family roles are adopted. This is an interesting arena. Hopf and Linstead (Fineman, 1993) discuss the "roles played" by members of organisations in the context of emotion. It leads me to consider what use organisations can make of work done on families and grief. If patterns of grief within families are similar to those within organisations then perhaps managers should understand these patterns in order to facilitate them.

One of the interviewees provided a good example of mutual support at work. His mother had died a month previously and he discussed with me how the hospice had treated him.

> Thinking about how the hospice has been for me, there were a number of things which struck me. One was no hassle about how much time I could have off, it was not mentioned, there was no bother about giving me the time and space .... I was off for three days ... when I came back there were cards expressing sympathy and I felt warmth ... a lot of people approached me and talked about it. I think that is quite important. There is space and permission to talk about the issues .... I haven't been pressurised.... If it

had been a hassle at work I would have just stopped coming ... it would have probably meant I would have been around less than I have been. Although I haven't worked to the optimum efficiency there has been no hassle. It's been quite supportive in a fairly unobtrusive way.

The role of mutual support is enhanced by encouragement of appreciation of one another, and a general ethos of tolerance and respect. Central to this will be the ability to listen well to one another. This will not only create an environment where mutual support is possible but will reduce the tendency to blame one another when under stress. This can be felt to be false and loses its value if it is imposed rather than genuine. Vachon writes about this when discussing anger. "Hugs were often expressions of warmth and loving but sometimes they were distorted expressions of anger and control". Even when it works, mutual support is not without its costs. The closeness between staff may lead to an intimacy which means each other's grief may have an emotional effect on one another. This was put well by the Middle Manager, who said, "you can be overwhelmed by other people's grief and it's not necessarily your own but it's how you manage and cope with other people's distress". Finally, it is important to remember managers need support in order to provide support.

Practical support and policies

There are a wide number of practical things organisations can do to create an environment where staff can deal with multiple deaths effectively for themselves and the organisation. It is important that these have a formal status and are perceived as a right and a responsibility within the organisation. They include formal staff support systems, stress management groups, allowing informal support, stated policies or statements relating to death, training, and leave from work when needed. Many of these have been identified in a document produced by the National Association of Staff Support, 'A Charter for Staff Support'. This is produced on the basis of the recognition that "Personal health care is often stressful, and over a period of time staff may become worn out or burnt out."

It is not unusual for organisations working with the dying to establish staff support groups. The organisation I worked for, which provided services to people with HIV, established a formal support group system on the basis that "Every workplace should be nourishing of its workers, providing structured opportunities for people to be paid attention to while they express their feelings". The basis for this was that "Research has shown conclusively that the capacity of people to sustain their commitment, enthusiasm and loving involvement in work of this kind is dependent on the quality of the support structures built into the workplace" (Memorandum from Director, December 1989). An hour and a half was built into everybody's working week to meet in a facilitated support group. The groups were established but proved less successful than hoped for. There appeared to be a number of reasons for this, including lack of space, work pressure, lack of safety in the groups and a lack of trust. This was borne out by the Nurse Educator in the hospice I visited.

> Staff support in various hospices is sometimes experienced as persecutory by the people it is intended to provide support and relief for. You then get into a vicious circle where people don't go, complain they are not supported and when asked why they don't attend support groups say they don't find them supportive.

I believe support groups do have their role. There are a number of ways of making them useful, such as allocated space and time structured into people's work routines. It is also important to note the focus of these groups. They need to address the emotional issues relating to loss, not organisational issues which can be a tendency in my experience. It is tempting to use them to 'gossip' or 'moan', but this is neither sustainable nor supportive. As Schoen writes, "Support groups are useful when carefully facilitated and focused on the content of the work and its relation to grief and not on other organizational issues" (Schoen, 1992, p 4). It is also vital that they are seen as important for all, not just for front-line workers. The Nurse Educator argued "it's something everybody does and it's not something just available for junior staff who are perceived as somehow or other unable to cope and therefore perceived as in need of support".

It might also be possible to liaise with other similar organisations about establishing systems to swap support for one another's staff. The Nurse Educator in the hospice explained such a system, "If staff have a bereavement they would be able to have counselling with a local hospital's occupational health department". Staff who might require some bereavement counselling often feel happier going to counsellors of organisations other than their own. This swapping system would also provide opportunities to discuss ideas about management of bereavement.

On a day-to-day level within the service itself there are systems which can be set up, such as handovers which include opportunities to talk briefly about how people feel. The Nurse Educator felt "one very simple thing people ought to do, especially clinical staff, is debrief at the end of shifts .... Then they can leave all the heavy stuff". Regular team building sessions which create a good environment for mutual support may also be helpful. These can provide an opportunity for people to learn from one another about mechanisms for coping and patterns which relate to the grieving process. I found that the more I understood what was going on for me, both by knowing about the theories and by hearing what my colleagues felt, the more I could see an end to the pain I was feeling.

Individual supervision from line managers can also be a useful tool in managing bereavement. The Charge Nurse had a very specific strategy.

> I make sure as far as I can that how they find out about the death is not a shock, that they don't overhear about it. That they find out because someone tells them in private. Then I check how they are with it. Are they feeling they did a good job with the person? Are they feeling fairly resolved? Or are they feeling they didn't go often enough, they let them down, that kind of stuff. Then I check practicalities like are they still working on different bits of it, or are they in the position where they have been busy in the run up, the person has died and now they're in the flat period, or are they still seeing the mother everyday and still in the busy phase .... Also practical things like are they going to the funeral on their own or do they want someone with them, and so on.

Individual supervision also provides an opportunity for staff to discuss how they feel about their work, to share responsibilities and as a way of monitoring the quality of their work which can be affected by grief.

Personnel policies can also enhance an environment within an organisation which reduces the incidence of burnout. These might include generous annual leave, flexible compassionate leave and formal systems of supervision and support. Framing the most appropriate policies is difficult because people differ. The Charge Nurse felt "The idea of a tariff of compassionate leave is difficult and dehumanising .... I tend to try and negotiate it with the person". There are no rules about how long a bereavement will take for a person to feel fully able to work. It is important that people are given the time they need, both within the organisation and in terms of compassionate leave. Some hospices have four-day weeks as a way of reducing stress and part-time work is often a useful option. Staff rotation may also be helpful and secondment elsewhere to reduce the exposure to the dying can help.

Policies allow for a formal explicit commitment to the management strategies I have outlined. If they are to be adopted they are best done so openly and explicitly. Well-developed and implemented policies can create a sense of mutual responsibility within organisations and require a commitment from all parties to carry them out.

Conclusion

The strategies I have outlined are by no means complete. I do not doubt that there are many ideas which could be added to what I hope are some useful recommendations for best practice. There are also a number of ways these strategies can be adapted, taking into account the context in which they are to be applied. I agree with the Nurse Educator who said "I think having a structured way of dealing with loss is a good idea and fine in theory but it is one of those areas where people do not operate according to theory and models". However, there are effective strategies, which are central to managing multiple bereavements. These strategies can be summarised as follows:

- Develop an understanding of the social context of death and dying and about theories concerning grief and loss.

- Develop self-awareness with regard to your own reaction to multiple bereavements.

- Consider people's motivations during the recruitment process and develop an induction and training programme which improves individual's resources for dealing with multiple bereavements.

- Create an atmosphere that allows the expression of emotion so that people can express their feelings about death freely.

- Challenge denial and acknowledge feelings so what is happening can be faced with integrity and left behind when appropriate.

- Consider the role of ritual within the organisation and apply and develop what is useful ritual.

- Consider the boundary issues that develop in this context, particularly with regard to the conflicts between involvement and detachment.

- Encourage mutual support in order to utilise all the human skills available to the organisation.

- Develop policies and practical systems of support to maximise the formal structural support available to staff and which reinforce these strategies.

Having identified some recommendations and strategies for best practice I still feel there is much more work to be done on emotions within organisations working with the dying. If there is anything useful to others that I have learnt in my experience of death and grieving it might be that we all do it differently and that prescriptions don't work. It would be good to develop a step-by-step management of death and loss in organisations, but this is not possible. Differences in individuals and organisational culture will profoundly affect strategies for best practice. If I had to say it in one sentence though, the key thing for me would be to encourage people to express their feelings and to allow them the safety and compassion to do so.

In consideration of what this means for the role of the manager in organisations working with the dying I return to my argument in the introduction, that organisations must be seen as an integral part of working people's lives and within a context. Managers have a responsibility for the emotional health and safety of staff as well as their physical health and safety.

Finally, it is vital that managers remember that they can't make the experience of multiple bereavements easy. The Charge Nurse I talked to spoke of

> ... a feeling that if you put enough in you can make anything palatable but you can't: that staff can have the loss without experiencing grief. That is almost implied by the support systems, that there won't be burn out because there won't be accumulated grief. That people won't have to say all this loss is too much and I don't want it.

Of course people will feel pain, they will find it difficult and will leave, but managers need to create the best systems and strategies they can in order to enable staff and themselves to work well, and without long-term emotional damage while experiencing multiple bereavements.

Postscript

Writing this paper was part of my own process of coming to terms with the emotions I have felt while managing in organisations working with the dying. It was very important for me to fully explore and to write down what I felt I was discovering about managing multiple bereavements. Having come to the end of this process and looking back on what I have written what occurs to me is how difficult it is to 'practice what I preach'. I find that applying the strategies I identify, in the organisation I am involved in, is extremely difficult. It is essentially about challenging not only the culture of the organisation but the deeply ingrained socialisation about death. Simply saying what people don't always wish to hear, for instance that 'many women do not survive breast cancer' is very difficult. People only want to talk about 'sad' things in a private corner, not as a group. Yet they do want to talk and seek me out to do so. I know getting this right will be a long slow process and the work I have done on this issue is part of this process.

References and further reading

Bell, J. (1993) *Doing your research project*, Buckingham: Open University Press.

Brown, K., Turner, J. (1989) *AIDS polices and programs for the workplace*, New York: Van Nostrand Reinhold.

Buckman, R. (1988) *I don't know what to say...*, London: Macmillan.

Charles-Edwards, D. (1992) *Death bereavement and work*, London: CEPEC.

Clark, D. (ed) (1993) *The future for palliative care*, Buckingham: Open University Press.

Clegg, S. (1990) *Modern organizations*, London: Sage Publications.

Coleman, G., Higgins, J., Smith, R., Tolan, F. (1990) *Training and development for resettlement staff*, Bristol: SAUS Publications.

Corr, C. and Corr, D. (eds) (1983) *Hospice care*, London: Faber & Faber.

Dowling, S. and Barrett, S. (1991) *Doctors in the making*, Bristol: SAUS Publications.

Enright, D.J. (1983) *The Oxford Book of Death*, Oxford: Oxford University Press.

Faulder, C. (1985) *Whose body is it?*, London: Virago Press.

Faulder, C. (1991) *A special gift*, London: Michael Joseph.

Fineman, S. (1993) *Emotion in organizations*, London: Sage.

Gittens, C. (ed) (1991) *Somebody said that word*, Lancashire: Littlewood Arc.

Glaser, B., Strauss, A. (1967) *The discovery of grounded theory*, London: Weidenfeld and Nicolson.

Guex, P. (1994) *An introduction to psycho-oncology*, London: Routledge.

James, N. (1989) 'Emotional labour: skill and work in the social regulation of feelings', *Sociological Review*, vol 37.

Jaques, E (1990) 'On the dynamics of social structure', *The Social Engagement of Social Science*, vol 1, The Socio-Psychological Perspective, pp 420-38, London: Free Association Books.

Kirkpatrick, B. (1988) *AIDS sharing the pain*, London: Darton, Longman and Todd.

Kubler-Ross, E. (1970) *On death and dying*, London: Tavistock Publications.

Kubler-Ross, E. (1981) *Living with death and dying*, London: Souvenir Press Ltd.

Levine, S. (1988) *Who dies?*, Bath: Gateway Books.

Lush, S. (1991) *Trinity Hospice – a history of care*, London: Trinity Hospice.

Marris, P. (1986) *Loss and change*, London: Routledge and Kegan Paul.

Maslach, C. (1982) *Burnout – the cost of caring*, New York: Prentice Hall Press.

Menzies Lyth, I. (1988) *Containing anxiety in institutions*, London: Free Association Books.

Menzies Lyth, I. (1990a) 'Social systems as a defence against anxiety', *The Social Engagement of Social Science*, vol 1, The Socio-Psychological Perspective, pp 438-62, London: Free Association Books.

Menzies Lyth, I. (1990b) 'A psychoanalytical perspective on social institutions', *The Social Engagement of Social Science*, vol 1, The Socio-Psychological Perspective, pp 463-75, London: Free Association Books.

Mordaunt, J. (1989) *Facing up to AIDS*, Dublin: O'Brien Press Ltd.

Moreland, L. and Legg, S. (1991) *Managing and funding AIDS organisations*, Compass Partnership, Department of Health.

Morgan, G. (ed) (1983) *Beyond method*, London: Sage Publications.

Morgan, G. (1986) *Images of organization*, London: Sage Publications.

Murray Parkes, C. (1986) *Bereavement*, London: Penguin Books.

Owens, R.G. and Naylor, F. (1989) *Living while dying*, London: Thorsons Publishers Ltd.

Pine, V.R. (1972) 'Social organization and death', OMEGA, vol 3 (2), pp 149-53.

Puckett, S. and Emery, A. (1988) *Managing AIDS in the workplace*, New York: Addison-Wesley Publishing Company Inc.

Reason, P. (ed) (1988) *Human inquiry in action*, London: Sage Publications.

Reason, P. and Marshall, J. (1987) 'Research as personal process', in Boud and Griffin (eds), *Appreciating adults learning: from the learners perspective*, London: Kogan Page.

Robbins, J. (ed) (1989) *Care of the dying patient*, London: Harper and Row.

Roberts, H. (ed) (1981) *Doing feminist research*, London: Routledge and Kegan Paul.

Rogers, C.R. (1951) *Client-centred therapy*, London: Constable.

Schoen, K. (1992) 'Managing grief in AIDS organizations', *Focus A Guide to AIDS Research and Counselling*, vol 7, no 6, pp 1-8.

Sontag, S. (1991a) *The way we live now*, London: Jonathan Cape.

Sontag, S. (1991b) *Illness as metaphor and AIDS and its metaphors*, London: Penguin Books.

Stroud, M. (1993) *Cancer help*, Oxford: Lion Publishing Plc.

Torbert, W.R. (1991) *The power of balance*, London: Sage Publications.

Trist, E., Higgin, H., Murray, H. and Pollock, A. (1990) 'The assumption of ordinariness as a denial mechanism', *The Social Engagement of Social Science*, vol 1, The Socio-Psychological Perspective, pp 476-93, London: Free Association Books.

Vachon, M., *Personality and lifestyle of hospice caregivers*, Toronto: Casey House Hospice Inc.

Wiley, J. (1990) 'The dramatisation of emotions in practice and theory: emotion work and emotion roles in a therapeutic community', *Sociology of Health and Illness*, 12 (2) pp 127-50.

Winn, D. (1987) *The hospice way*, London: Macdonald and Co Ltd.

Worden, J.W. (1987) *Grief counselling and grief therapy*, London: Tavistock Publications.